MACHINERY'S REFERENCE SERIES

EACH NUMBER IS ONE UNIT IN A COMPLETE
LIBRARY OF MACHINE DESIGN AND SHOP
PRACTICE REVISED AND REPUB-
LISHED FROM MACHINERY

NUMBER 25

DEEP HOLE DRILLING

SECOND EDITION

CONTENTS

Deep-hole Drilling
Deep-Hole Drill

reprinted by Lindsay Publications Inc - all rights reserved

3 4 5 6 7 8 9 0 - 2001 - ISBN 1-55918-258-X

Introduction

The difficulties to be overcome in producing deep drilled holes can be classified in three groups. In the first place the drill has a great tendency to "run out," thus producing a hole that is neither straight, nor uniform in diameter; in the second place great difficulties are encountered in trying to remove the chips in a satisfactory manner, and in the third place the heating of the cutting tool is difficult to prevent.

The principle involved in common drill presses where the drill is given a rotary motion simultaneously with the forward motion for feeding is the one least adapted to produce a straight and true hole. Better results are obtained by giving only a rotary motion to the drill, and feeding the work toward it. It has been found, however, that for drilling deep holes the reversal of this, that is, imparting a rotary motion to the work, and the feed motion to the drill will answer the purpose still better. It seems as if there could be no material difference between the two latter methods. An analysis of the conditions involved will show,

however, that there is a decided difference in the action of the drill. If the drill rotates, and the work is fed forward as shown to the left in Fig. 1, the drill, when deviating from its true course, will be caused to increase its deviation still more, by the wedge action of the part B, which tends to move in the direction BA when the work is fed forward. In the case of the work rotating and the drill being fed forward, as shown to the right in Fig. 1, the point of the drill when not running true will be carried around by the work in a circle with the radius a, thus tending to bend the drill in various directions. The drill is by this action forced back into the

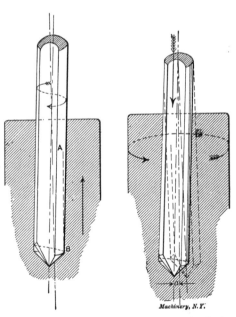

Fig. 1. Comparison between Action of Cutting Tool when Drill and when Work revolves

course of "least resistance," as it is evident that the bending action, being exerted on the drill in all directions, will tend to carry the point back to the axis of the work where no bending action will appear. The chips, as is well known, are carried off by forcing a fluid into the hole, which upon its return carries with it the chips. This fluid being oil will serve the double purpose of carrying away the chips and lubricating the cutting tool, keeping it at a normal temperature.

In the following chapters we shall deal with the practice of deep hole drilling as met with in a number of prominent American shops, presenting at the same time a collection of useful data covering different classes of work. The relation between ordinary drilling and deep hole drilling, dealing with first and fundamental principles, is treated in Chapter I, followed by a detailed account of the practice of deep hole drilling at the Pratt & Whitney Works, Hartford, Conn. In Chapter II the boring of large guns, according to the practice employed at the Watervliet Arsenal, is described. Chapter III is devoted to illustrating and describing various constructions of deep hole drills of merit, together with hints regarding their making, thereby completing the treatise.

CHAPTER I

Principles of Deep Hole Drilling

The process of drilling deep holes in metal is a familiar one in many shops, particularly where firearms are manufactured, or heavy ordnance is constructed. Since the adoption of hollow spindles for lathes and other machine tools, the methods for machining the bores of guns have been employed in machine tool shops for drilling these spindles; and through this and other means the principles of the operation have become better understood. It is not an easy matter, however, even with the best appliances, to drill or bore a, deep hole smooth and round, of exactly the required diameter from end to end, and perfectly straight. While many mechanics are familiar in a general way with the methods and tools for doing this work, specific information upon the subject will be appreciated by those who have not had actual experience in deep hole drilling.

It is well known that a long, or deep, hole—that is, one long in proportion to its diameter— is best roughed out and finished by using a tool on the end of a long bar which enters the work from one end. This is true, whether drilling into solid metal, or boring and reaming a

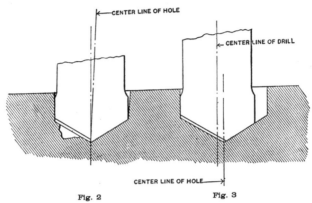

CENTER LINE OF HOLE

CENTER LINE OF DRILL

CENTER LINE OF HOLE

Fig. 2   Fig. 3

hole that has already been drilled or bored out. A boring bar which extends through the piece, and on which is either a stationary or a traveling head, is not satisfactory for very long work, owing to the spring and deflection of the bar, which is made worse by the fact that the bar must be enough smaller than the bore to allow room for the cutter head. While a long hole may sometimes be finished satisfactorily by means of such a boring bar, by packing the cutter head with wooden blocks which just fill the part of the bore that has been machined, and so support the bar, the method is fundamentally incorrect for long work.

The best methods for machining deep holes are nothing more nor less than an adaptation of what has been found successful in ordinary drilling and boring in the engine lathe or chucking machine. We will therefore first discuss certain types of chucking tools and drills, and show their relationship to tools that may be used for deep hole drilling.

The Flat Drill

To start with first principles, consider the ordinary flat drill. It is useful for rough work or in drilling hard metals, because it can be easily made and tempered; but it has too much of an inclination for drilling holes that are neither round nor straight, and whose diameter seems to bear no relation to the diameter of the drill. When a flat drill runs into a blow hole or strikes a hard spot, it is deflected, as in Fig. 2, the only resistance to this deflection being the narrow edges of the drill. Under such conditions the hole will be out of round, and crooked. Add to this natural tendency of a flat drill to run out the fact that such drills are often carelessly made, and one understands why they

4

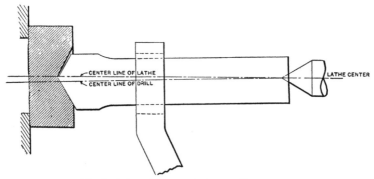

Fig. 4. Action of Improperly Ground Chucking Drill

have a reputation for poor work. Thus, if the point is not in line with the axis of the drill, and if the lips are of unequal length, or do not make equal angles with the axis, the hole will be larger than the drill diameter. This is illustrated in Fig. 3, where one lip is longer than the other, and the point does not lie in the central axis of the drill. The tendency of the drill is to rotate about its point, and thus the axis will move in a small circle about this point, causing the hole to be of larger diameter than the drill.

It is obvious that to improve the action of a flat drill, it should be so guided as to prevent its wabbling and to compel it to move forward in a straight line. This is partially accomplished with the flat chucking drill, which is a near relative of the ordinary flat drill, differing from it in that it is generally more carefully made and is adapted for use in the engine lathe. In Fig. 4 is an illustration of a chucking drill at work on a piece in the lathe, and to make the comparison fair it is shown with one lip longer than the other, as was the flat drill in Fig. 3. The work is held in the lathe chuck and turns with the spindle. A rest steadies the drill at a point near the work, and in starting the hole, the drill is held firmly against the rest by means of a monkey wrench. It will be noted that while a poorly ground chucking drill will make a large hole, just as does the drill in Fig. 3, if properly started it will not wabble, and it will drill the hole where it is wanted and approximately in line with the lathe centers. To attain these results, however, the drill must be started right. If it is found to wabble when left free, it must be started over again, before the full size of the hole has been attained, by crowding it into the work and toward the operator at the same time, causing only one edge of the drill to do the cutting. This edge will then true up the hole, and in proceeding with the drilling the trued hole will guide the drill. The latter will thus be continuously supported near the cutting edges by the cylindrical surface of the hole drilling. The drill from which the illustration was made was employed for drilling a four-inch hole through steel rolls seven feet long. Instead of depending upon the narrow edges

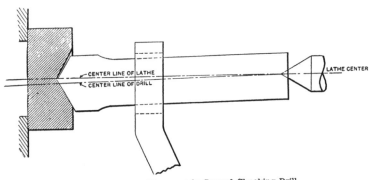

Fig. 4. Action of Improperly Ground Chucking Drill

hole, and the drill will tend to advance in the direction in which it was started. After the hole is drilled, it is usually brought to size by a flat reamer, like Fig. 5. For reasons that will be explained, the flat drill is not an accurate tool, even when well made and used in the lathe, and the flat reamer is not as reliable as one with more blades. The general principle, however, of first starting with a true hole, and then having the drill body designed to follow in its path and so guide the cutting edges, is the fundamental principle of deep hole drilling. Fig. 6 shows how a flat drill may be adapted for deep of the drill proper to guide and support the cutting edges, the cutting edges are formed on a blade inserted in a cylindrical cast-iron head, the outside diameter of which is turned to a sliding fit in the hole that is being bored. The cutting edges are grooved to break up the chips, enabling the latter to pass out through the passage E, on each side of the head. The grooves are laid out so that those in one blade come opposite to the lands in the other blade. In the illustration, A is the cutter, B one of the screws holding the cutter to the head C, and the head is attached to the bar by the shank D.

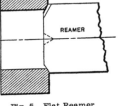

Fig. 5. Flat Reamer

The Twist Drill

The modern twist drill accomplishes all that is attained by the arrangement in Fig. 6, and in addition can be ground without seriously affecting the rake, and will free itself from chips more readily, owing to its spiral flutes. The lands of a twist drill present a large cylindrical surface to bear against the sides of the hole and take the side thrust. If the drill is also guided by a hardened bushing, at the point where it enters the metal, as in the case of jig work, the drill will have very little chance to deflect, and the hole will be necting with the grooves in the drill, as indicated. The shank can be threaded and fitted to a metal tube which acts as a boring bar and through which the chips and oil may pass from the point of the drill. Oil is conveyed to the point on the outside of the tube, as shown in Fig. 7.

In using the hollow drill, the hole is first started by means of a short drill of the size of the hole desired, and drilled to a depth equal to the length of the hollow drill to be employed. The body of the hollow drill acts as a stuffing, compelling the oil to follow the oil grooves provided, and the chips to flow out through the flutes and the hol-

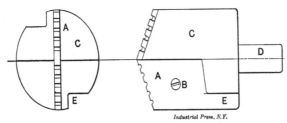

Industrial Press, N.Y.

Fig. 6. Flat Drill with Inserted Blade for Deep Drilling

accurately located and will be quite true and straight. The twist drill in a modified form is also employed for deep hole drilling. The hollow drill introduced by the Morse Twist Drill Co., New Bedford, Mass., is adapted for this purpose, and in Fig. 7 is shown the arrangement recommended by this company for feeding this drill into the work. The drill has a hole lengthwise through the shank, con- low shank. The methods of supporting and driving the work, and of feeding the drill, are clearly shown in Fig. 7. Drills of this type are regularly manufactured in sizes up to three inches in diameter, and it is stated that the best results are obtained, when drilling tool steel, by revolving the drill at a cutting speed of 20 feet per minute, with a feed of 0.0025 inch per revolution, while machine steel will admit of a cutting speed of 40 feet per minute and a feed of 0.0035 inch per revolution.

Number of Cutting Edges Desirable

When drilling a hole out of solid stock, some type of drill having two lips or cutting edges is usually the most feasible, and probably nothing will be devised that on the whole surpasses the twist drill for such work. As is well known, the ordinary twist drill is always provided with two flutes, but twist drills having three or more flutes have been devised, made and tried. The advantages gained by adding to the number of cutting edges have, however, not been great enough to justify the increased cost of manufacture. When added to this comes the weakness caused by the increased number of grooves, and the complicated operation of correctly grinding such drills, it is clear why drills having two flutes only have been and should be adopted.

An end mill, like that in Fig. 11, can be used for drilling, if it has a "center cut," and it will presently be explained how a tool with a single cutting edge may be advantageously employed, particularly for deep hole drilling. The familiar D-drill is of this type, and also its modification as used by the Pratt & Whitney Co. in drilling gun barrels.

When it comes to truing up or enlarging a hole previously drilled or bored, the two-lip drill is not suitable in any of its forms. For boring a true hole nothing can surpass a single-pointed boring tool, the ideal condition for finishing a hole being when the cutting point is a real diamond, or a rotating wheel of abrasive material.

It is obvious that when a hard or soft spot is encountered in boring with a tool having a single cutting edge, only that particular place is affected by the spring of the tool; while with a double cutter, as shown in Fig. 9, first sketch, any deflection due to irregularities, such as at *a* or *b*, will cause the tool to spring and the cutting edge on the opposite side to introduce similar irregularities in the opposite side of the hole. This is one objection to the two-lip drill for accurate work. With three points the tool is somewhat better supported when a high place is encountered, as shown in the second sketch, Fig. 9, and when a cutting point strikes a low place the other two edges are not moved away from their position so much as if they were opposite the first edge. Hence a tool with three edges should prove better than one with two, and one with four, being better supported, would seem better on this account

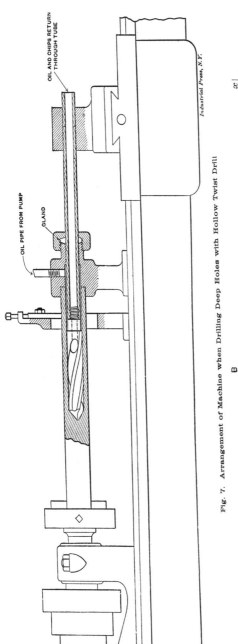

OIL AND CHIPS RETURN THROUGH TUBE

OIL PIPE FROM PUMP

GLAND

Industrial Press, N.Y.

Fig. 7. Arrangement of Machine when Drilling Deep Holes with Hollow Twist Drill

END VIEW

Industrial Press, N.Y.

OIL DUCT

B

A

SECTION AT A-B

x— HARDENED STEEL STRIPS DOVETAILED IN AND GROUND TO SIZE

Fig. 8. D-drill with Inserted Blade, used for Deep Hole Drilling

9

than one with three, but has the disadvantage of opposite cutters. Five edges ought to give still better results.

In Fig. 10 is shown a four-grooved chucking drill which is suitable for truing up either a drilled hole or a cored hole, but obviously it cannot be used for drilling out solid stock. It has less tendency to "run out" than a two-lip drill, and the edges are less likely to catch under the scale or in breaking through, since each has only half the depth of cut to take.

In general, it may be said that in boring the best results are obtained when the tool has a single cutting edge, but if it is

the boring tool over the multi-blade reamer. A reamer sometimes refuses to produce a perfectly round hole, and will do this whether the number of teeth is odd or even. The writer has seen the photograph of the bore of a 12-inch gun that had been reamed out with an eleven-sided reamer, and the bore had eleven distinct sides, clearly visible in the photograph. The trouble was overcome by spacing the reamer teeth unequally.

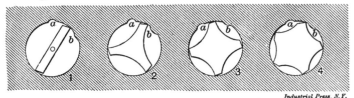

Fig. 9. Effect of the Number of Cutting Edges

Advantages of the End Cut

One trouble with reamers, however, is that the teeth necessar-

Fig. 10. Four-lip Drill for Cored Holes

desirable to have more cutting edges, a tool with several will be more satisfactory than one with only two. Any machinist who has tried to true up the taper hole in a lathe spindle, first by boring and then by reaming, will appreciate the superiority of

ily cut on their side edges instead of on their ends, and the whole effect of any unevenness in the hole is to crowd the reamer to one side. The condition exists to a less extent with a flat or twist drill, where the cutting edges are at an angle with the center line, and the resultant of any unusual pressure is felt partly as a side thrust and partly as an end thrust. Now, by making a drill to cut squarely on its end and but very little, or not at all, on its sides, the side thrust is mostly done

edge should be slightly rounded to help support the cutter and prevent chattering, and the width *A* of the cutting edge should be from 1/32 to 1/16 inch less than the radius of the hole to be drilled. The objection to this tool is that it cannot be

Fig. 11. End Mill with Center Cut, suitable for Accurate Drilling

away with. The end mill shown in Fig. 11 is a good illustration of such a tool, and it is known to be capable of boring very accurate holes when used for that purpose in the milling machine. In Fig. 12 is a boring tool with a

supported stiffly enough by the tool-post for a hole of great depth, and for this purpose the D-drill shown in Fig. 13, and which works on the same principle, is well adapted. In its simplest form it consists of a round

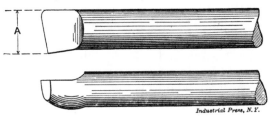

Fig. 12. Boring Tool with the Cutting Edge on the End

single cutting edge, which cuts on its end and is capable of drilling a true hole in solid metal. It consists of a round tool steel bar, with one end flattened and ground to form a cutting edge, as shown. It is designed to be held in the tool-post of the lathe, in a position perpendicular to the face-plate. The inner edge or corner of the cutting

bar of the diameter of the hole to be drilled, one-quarter to one-half of which is milled out to give a passage for the chips. The end of the bar is shaped with a cutting edge on one side, extending almost or quite to the center, and with the other side relieved to give clearance for the cutter. Such a drill should be supported by a bearing close to

11

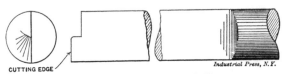

CUTTING EDGE

Industrial Press, N.Y.

Fig. 13. D-drill used for Deep Drilling

the hole to be bored, in case it is to start the hole itself, and it is better yet to start the hole with a twist drill and true it up with a single-pointed boring tool, and then let the drill be guided by this hole. This is the surest way of getting a hole concentric with the axis of the lathe. As the bar is of the same diameter as the hole, the cutter will be supported by one-half the surface of the hole, and if it is once started right in an accurate hole, it will continue in the right direction.

It is desirable to have the cutter blade separated from the bar or head, as the case may be, so that it may be renewed or removed for grinding, particularly in drilling large holes. In Fig. 8 is an illustration of such a cutter head as used by a large ship- and engine-building concern, in drilling propeller shafts. The body of the cutter is made from soft steel with tool steel strips x dove-tailed in and ground in place to size. The cutters are made by jigs and are interchangeable, and their shape is such as to break up the chips, which are washed out by the force of oil supplied by a pump, through the hollow boring bar,

to which this cutter head is fastened. One of these cutters, four inches in diameter, has bored 12 inches in a piece of nickel steel in one hour, cutting a fair and smooth hole, and no trouble has ever occurred, even when holes have been drilled to a depth of 32 feet.

Rotating Work vs. Rotating Drill

In deep hole drilling it is customary to have the drill fixed so that it cannot turn and rotate the work, following the usual method in this respect for boring accurate holes in the lathe. Since the outer end of the work can be supported in the center rest, it is always possible to make the work run true, while it is not so easy to make a drill run true and coincident with the axis of the work. The difference in principle involved has already been explained in the introduction and shown graphically in Fig. 1.

Deep Hole Drilling Attachment for the Lathe

An attachment is shown in Fig. 14 for performing deep

drilling rapidly and economically on the engine lathe. This attachment is built by the Lodge & Shipley Machine Tool Co., Cincinnati, Ohio. It consists essentially of a drill spindle, mounted on the cross-slide in place of the usual tool-post, in combination with an electric motor and suitable gearing for rotating the method of rotating the work, and at the same time to give the high cutting speed of which high-speed tools are capable, without necessitating a high rate of revolution for the heavy spindle and gearing of the lathe.

The drill spindle bearing, with the bracket on which the motor is mounted, is cast as one

Fig. 14. Lodge & Shipley Motor-driven Attachment for Deep Drilling in the Lathe

spindle. A support is provided for holding the outer end of the work, the other end of which is clamped in the chuck or face-plate of the lathe. Provision is also made for forcing a copious supply of lubricant to the point of the drill used. The purpose of the attachment is to make it possible to drill a hole true with the center line by the usual piece with the bed-plate. This plate is bolted to the wings or arms of the carriage. The 3-horsepower 2 to 1 variable speed motor shown, is connected to the drill spindle through an intermediate raw-hide gear. The spindle is bored to supply lubrication to the drill; it has a large bearing, and is ring oiled. The drill shank is fitted to the hole in the spindle by reducing bushings. The outer end of the drill is carried in a free bushing, revolving in a support bolted to the lathe bed. The drill used is of the special construction known as the "Chard" deep drill. A flat blade of high speed steel is held in position at the end of a steel shank by a tapered pin; it is so ground as to break up the chips and thus-facilitate their removal. Lubrication under pressure sufficient to clear the chips and cool the cutting edge is supplied by a pump attached to the lathe at the rear of the head-stock, and driven from the lathe countershaft. Flexible tubing connects this pump with the hollow spindle through a nipple at the rear. Two copper tubes, flush with the surface of the drill, carry the lubricant to the cutting edge. This type of drill has been in use for some time on lathe spindles, back gear sleeves and pulley sleeves. Under favorable conditions a 2-inch drill has been advanced at the rate of 2 1/4 inches per minute. The drill is illustrated and described in Chapter III.

This whole attachment may be easily removed from the carriage by the use of an over-head crane, suitable I-bolts being provided for this purpose. Only a few minutes times is required to change the machine over for engine lathe work. The particular device illustrated is used regularly for drilling holes in locomotive driving axles, the holes being 1 inch in diameter and 44 inches deep.

Drilling Deep Holes by the Pratt & Whitney Method.

A highly satisfactory drill for use in drilling deep holes is one brought out by the Pratt & Whitney Co., principally for use in connection with their gun-barrel drilling machines. The tool in question is a development of the old D- or hog-nose drill, already described, which has one cutting lip only. It is carefully ground on the outside,

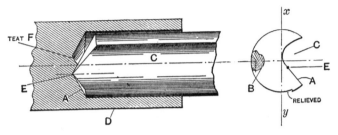

Fig. 15. Pratt & Whitney Co.'s Deep Hole Drill

and is supplied with an oil duct through which oil at high pressure may be brought directly to the cutting edge.

Referring to Fig. 15, A is the cutting edge, B the oil duct, and C the chip groove. In milling the latter groove, the cutter is brought directly to the center line, so that in this respect the drill is very free-cutting as compared with the ordinary two-lip twist drill which has a central web. In the end view, the shape of the chip groove is clearly indicated. The cutting edge A is radial. In sharpening the drill, to the drill, which, owing to its periphery being partly relieved, would have a tendency to travel in a curve away from its cutting side.

The piece being drilled is run at very high speed, the periphery speed at the outer diameter of the hole being as high as 130 feet per minute on machine steel. The feed, however, is quite fine, on a 0.3-inch drill averaging 0.0004 inch per revolution, while on a 3-inch drill it is about 0.0008 inch. These figures, of course, are dependent to a great extent on the material being

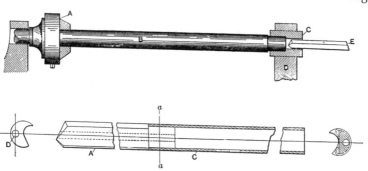

Fig. 16. Arrangement for Starting the Deep Hole Drill, and Method of Fastening Shank to Drill

the high point or part first entering the work is not ground in the center as is usually the case in drills, but to one side as shown in Fig. 15, in which D is a cross-section of the work being drilled, and E the high point of the drill. Grinding the drill in this manner makes possible its running true or straight, the teat F on the work acting as a support drilled. The drills are made of high-grade steel and left very hard, so that the fine feed has little tendency to glaze the cutting edge.

The piece being drilled is held and revolved at one end by a suitable chuck on the live spindle of the machine, while the other end, which should be turned perfectly true, runs in a stationary bushing having at its outer end a hole the diameter of the drill. The drill enters the work through the bushing, and is thus started perfectly true. The arrangement is indicated in oil, of course, is used over and over again, and with a large reservoir will be kept quite cool.

The drill is made up of the drill tip and shank, the tip varying in length from 4 inches to 8

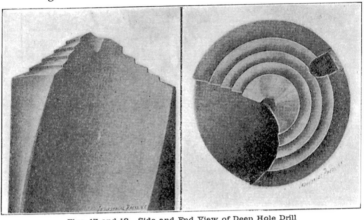

Figs. 17 and 18. Side and End View of Deep Hole Drill

the upper view in Fig. 16, in which A represents the chuck, B the work, C the bushing, D the support for holding the bushing, and E the drill. Through the oil duct of the drill, oil is forced at a pressure varying from 150 to 200 pounds per square inch. After passing the cutting edge, the oil returns to the reservoir by the way of the chip groove, forcing the chips along in its travel. In drills of large diameter, especially when working on tough, stringy material, the cutting edge is usually ground so as to produce a number of shavings, instead of one the full width of the cutting lip, so that no trouble is experienced in getting chips out of the way. The inches, while the length of shank is determined by the depth of hole that is to be drilled. The lower view in Fig. 16 will clearly illustrate the construction of a small, complete drill, A being the tip, C the shank, and D the oil duct. The shanks on small drills are made from steel tubing, rolled as shown in the cross-section at the right-hand end. The tip is carefully fitted and soldered to the shank, which, it should be noted, is a little smaller in diameter than the tip.

The relief or clearance of the cutting edge of the drill, the amount the "high point" of the drill should be off center, and the number of rings on the end of the drill, when provided with notches for breaking up the chips, depend entirely upon the material that is to be drilled. For instance, on very soft stock, the supporting teat should be more substantial than on hard spindle or gun steel, so that it is evident that on soft stock the high point should be more off center or nearer to the outer diameter, than on hard stock. Figs. 17 and 18 are reproductions from actual photographs of a 3-inch drill, and the reader will obtain a very clear idea from the engravings of the appearance of

made very slightly tapering toward the shank to free itself. As previously stated, in milling the chip groove the cutter is brought exactly to the center of the drill. When hardening and grinding, however, the location frequently changes slightly so that the groove does not come to the center of the drill. In such cases it is necessary to grind out the lip at the point as shown in the illustrations made from photographs in Figs. 17 and 18. Generally the operator grinds this a little beyond the center,

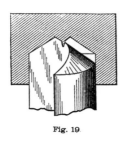

Fig. 19.

Fig. 20

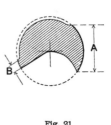

Fig. 21

gravings of the appearance of the tool described. These figures illustrate a drill ground on the end so as to produce several shavings.

The present practice in relieving the large drills is shown in Fig. 21. The straight, or radial, edge is the cutting edge of the drill and the distance *B* is about 1/8 inch on a one-inch drill. The surface *A* is left of the full radius of the drill, and makes a good back rest. When the drill is ground on its periphery, it is

but no trouble results, as the small teat produced thereby is broken off when the bottom of the ground out place comes in contact with the end of the teat, as indicated in Figs. 19 and 20.

In Fig. 22 is an engraving of one size of a tube and gun-barrel drilling machine, as built by the Pratt & Whitney Co., Hartford., Conn. This machine, while primarily designed for drilling gun barrels, is adapted for any class of deep hole drilling, such as hollow spindles, etc. The ma-

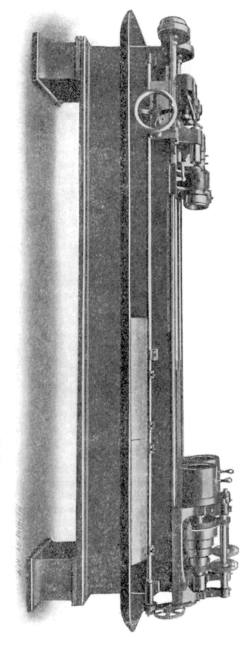

Fig. 22. Pratt & Whitney Co.'s Tube and Gun-barrel Drilling Machine

chine is provided with a double head, the heads being placed side by side at one end as shown; independent spindles are mounted in each head. On their inner ends are chucks for securing and rotating the work, which is also supported by split bushings carried in rests on the bed. The drills are carried by the carriages, and fed positively by power feed. This feed is variable, to provide for different qualities of stock to be drilled. Two rotary pumps, one for each head, force oil, supplied from a tank placed underneath the machine, through a series of tubes into and through the drill. The oil lubricates the cutting lip and forces out the chips into the basin on the top of the tank, where they are drained, and from where the strained oil is returned to the tank again.

Attention should also be called to the method employed for drilling oil holes in so-called oil twist drills. These holes are drilled before the drill is fluted, the tool afterwards being rough fluted with straight flutes, and then twisted, and finally finished in the usual manner. The drilling of the oil holes is done progressively by small twist drills, arranged in order of length, each drill deepening the hole made by its predecessor only 1/2 or 3/4 inch. The hole is begun by a short stiff drill which starts the hole perfectly true, and the following drills are guided by the sections of the hole first drilled, This practice eliminates the use of a long, slender drill for drilling the first part of the hole, and enables the drilling to be done much faster than would otherwise be possible.

Chapter II

Deep Hole Drilling In Gun Construction

It is generally known among well-informed mechanics that the introduction of built-up or hooped guns necessitated many new designs and radical changes in machine tools, especially In the lathe. This chapter is intended to elucidate the methods of deep horizontal boring and reaming in the manner these operations are met with in the

roughing and finishing boring of the tubes for modern built-up steel guns. These tubes, which constitute the central portion of the guns, and upon which a series of hoops are shrunk, are made of a very high quality of special oil-tempered steel. The tubes, according to requirements for the various sizes of guns, usually vary in length from 20 to 50 feet, with internal diameters from 6 to 30 inches, for the large guns, and from 5 to 15 feet in length, with internal diameters from 3 to 6 inches, for the smaller sizes.

As it is primarily essential that the bore of these tubes be perfectly straight and the diameter correct and uniform, approaching mathematical accuracy, it might be of interest to point out the simplicity of design and performance of the subjected. After having ascertained the amount of existing warp and having investigated the concentricity of the inner and outer circumferences, the tube is centered and spotted in a special lathe designated for the purpose, preparatory to the first rough boring. The tool used in rough boring, commonly known as the hog-nose tool, and represented in Fig. 23, consists of a semi-circular cast-iron body provided with a shank on one

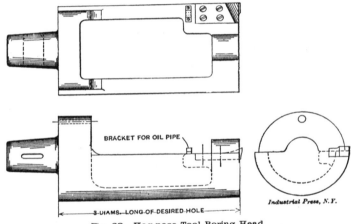

Fig. 23. Hog-nose Tool Boring Head

tools with which this most important operation is performed. The forgings for the tubes as received from the steel works have a surplus amount of metal on the inside and outside, to allow for the boring and turning operations. Owing to the length being so great in comparison with the diameter, they are also, in the majority of cases, more or less warped, due to the end secured to the front end of the boring bar (which has a taper and flat keyhole to receive it, Fig. 24); and a cutter clamped on the forward end, the material of which is high-grade tool steel, very carefully tempered. The cutter is made with the edge cutting square on the forward end, and with the lip turned slightly upward, in order to roll the chips backward, as indicated in Fig. 25.

Provision is made to throw a jet of a lubricating mixture in front of the tools during the operations of boring, reaming, and finishing, the lubricant serving to diminish the friction on the tools as well as to preserve their temper. This is accomplished by a rotary oil pump which conveys a continuous stream of oil by means of two wrought-iron pipes connected

is removed, and the tool shown in Fig. 26, for finishing and reaming, is inserted in its place. This is made of a cast-iron body about four diameters in length,

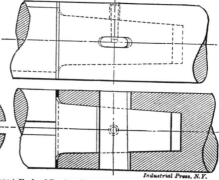

Fig. 24. Front End of Boring Bar showing Method of Attaching Boring Head

with an intermediate flexible metallic hose which travels with the boring bar and is attached to a fixed pipe which passes through the interior of the boring bar, terminating at the end of the cutting tools. The pump is provided with different changes of speed.

Although this tool, because of its design, is capable of removing a considerable quantity of metal, it has proved most practical not to allow it (though this is seldom required) to remove more than from 0.2 to 0.5 inch of metal on the side, leaving approximately 0.01 inch to be removed by the reaming and finishing tool in the succeeding operations.

The rough boring being completed, the hog-nosed tool

to which are bolted two semi-circular blocks of carefully selected and well seasoned oak or maple that have been previously submerged for a long period in a bath of lard oil and that serve

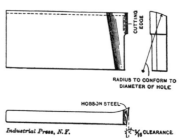

Fig. 25. Detail of the Boring Tool

as guides for the cutters bolted to the front end of the head, as shown in detail in Fig. 26. These blocks, while in position, are turned off to a diameter about 0.005 inch larger than the desired bore, the idea being to

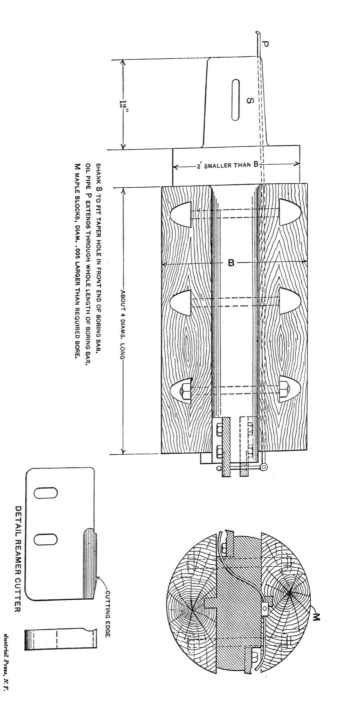

SHANK S TO FIT TAPER HOLE IN FRONT END OF BORING BAR.
OIL PIPE P EXTENDS THROUGH WHOLE LENGTH OF BORING BAR.
M MAPLE BLOCKS, DIAM. .005 LARGER THAN REQUIRED BORE.

12"

2' SMALLER THAN B

ABOUT 4 DIAMS. LONG

B

P

S

M

DETAIL REAMER CUTTER

CUTTING EDGE

Fig. 26. Tool for Finishing and Reaming Holes in Large Guns

dustrial Press, N.Y.

22

force them in and thus give them a smooth and uniform bearing surface. The cutters used are made from a very high-grade steel, ground to exact size, and oilstoned to conform to the required diameters.

To insure a perfect alignment for the tool before commencing the actual reaming, it is good practice to counterbore the tubes from 3 to 6 inches deep. The method of supplying oil while reaming is the same as employed in the operation of rough boring. It may be of interest to note that, with the same cutting speed, the feed may be from four to five times. that of the hog-nosed feed, by

also serves to maintain the size in case the forward part of the cutter becomes slightly worn.

Multiple cutter wood reamers, illustrated in Fig. 27, have been successfully used for bores of from 3- to 6-inch caliper, for lengths varying from 5 to 15 feet. Greater feed can be employed with tools thus constructed, and consequently considerable time is saved by their use. It must be borne in mind, however, that in tubes of great length, in which there is an unequal distribution of stock on the interior, these tools have a tendency to run out of their true axis, thus leaving an unsymmetrical bore. This difficulty is

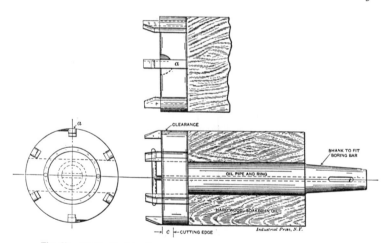

Fig. 27. Boring Tool for Holes of from Three to Six Inches in Diameter

giving the cutter a taper in front of about 1 to 10 ,with a straight cutting edge 1 inch long on the side. (See detail of reamer cutter in Fig. 26.) Such construction

obviated and a perfect and uniform bore obtained, by the use of the previously described hog-nosed tool and wood-lined reamer, although some time is

23

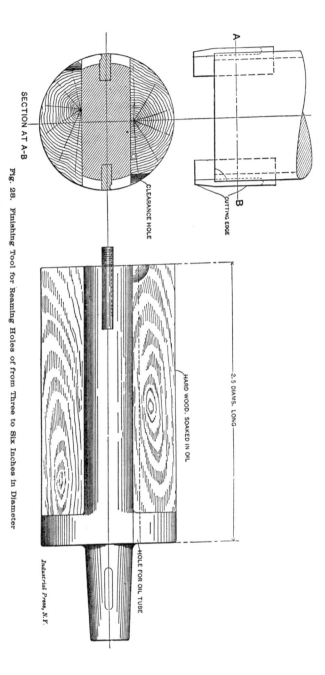

SECTION AT A-B

CLEARANCE HOLE

CUTTING EDGE

A

B

HARD WOOD. SOAKED IN OIL

2.5 DIAMS. LONG

HOLE FOR OIL TUBE

Fig. 28. Finishing Tool for Reaming Holes of from Three to Six Inches in Diameter

Industrial Press, N.Y.

24

sacrificed owing to the reduced feeds at which they have to be run compared with the feeds obtainable with a multiple cutter wood reamer.

In boring guns, lathes are employed which are specially designed for the purpose. Nevertheless, if such a machine is not available, for short lengths and small bores, it is advisable to use the old and well-known method of attaching to the cross-slide of a common lathe of suitable length of bed a fixed support or bracket having a bore to receive a number of bushes, the bores of which correspond to the varying diameters of boring bars. The hub of this support or bracket has one side split to enable it to be tightened by a bolt, in order to retain and grip the bushing which is likewise split for the purpose of gripping the boring bar. The boring and reaming tools shown in the engravings, Figs. 27 and 28, are particularly applicable in this case. After having determined the required feed and set the lathe in motion, the carriage will serve to feed the bar in the usual manner. The other functions are performed in the ordinary way and are too obvious for further explanation.

Machines Employed in Boring Large Guns

While, as just mentioned, any lathe may be employed for deep hole drilling, when large guns are bored, use is made of machines especially designed for the purpose. In the following is shown and described the general design of the boring and turning lathe employed at the Government Army Gun Factory, at Watervliet Arsenal, N.Y., for performing the necessary operations in connection with a 16-inch breechloading rifle. Of course, only the most characteristic features of this huge lathe can be dwelt upon.

Before entering upon a description of the lathe, however, a few explanatory words with reference to the gun constructed may be in place. The semi-longitudinal section in the upper part of Fig. 29 will serve to explain the method of assembling the built-up or hooped gun, which is composed of several parts united to form a whole. The parts are properly arranged to support the stresses upon them, and the gun has therefore been termed "built-up or hooped." These parts are assembled according to modern practice adopted by the ordnance department, for which purpose the army gun factory is equipped with specially-designed oil and high-pressure steam shrinkage furnaces. Preparatory to shrinkage, all parts constituting the gun have been subjected to various accurate

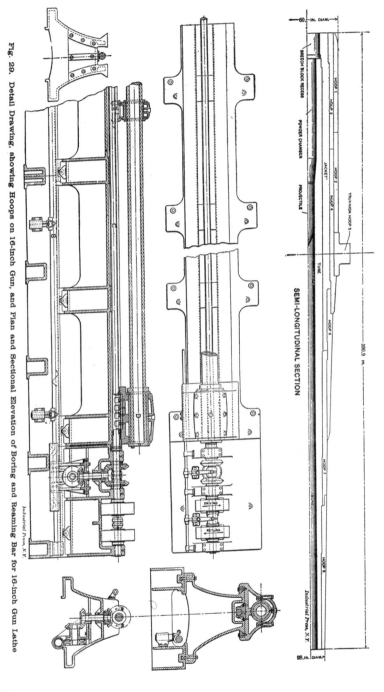

Fig. 29. Detail Drawing, showing Hoops on 16-inch Gun, and Plan and Sectional Elevation of Boring and Reaming Bar for 16-inch Gun Lathe

Industrial Press, N.Y.

and particular operations performed by special machines and have been measured with exact instruments and gages designed and made at the army gun factory, for ascertaining the required dimensions. The central portion of the gun is called the tube, upon which are shrunk the series of hoops. The jacket is shrunk on the rear portion of the tube, overhanging the tube a certain distance to form the breech recess. The tube and jacket are made of nickel steel, the remaining hoops being of fluid compressed steel containing no nickel. After the ingots for the tube, jacket and hoops have been forged on mandrels under hydraulic pressure, they are tempered and annealed, in order to give them the desired physical qualities.

The lathe for boring the tubes for this gun consists of the bed, headstock, two tool carriages, muzzle, intermediate, and breech rests, and a boring bar with carriage and four supports, as shown in Fig. 29. The main bed is 44 feet long by 9 feet 10 inches wide, made in two sections. The boring bar carriage bed is 67 feet long and 6 feet wide, and is made in three sections. All sections are firmly joined by taper bolts. The weight of the whole lathe is 280 tons. There are two similar tool carriages provided with a hand lever by which the leadscrew nut is engaged and disengaged. The lower lateral slide traverses the length of the main bed by means of a feed-screw, or by the use of a ratchet wrench. On this slide is the lower cross-slide, and on the intermediate cross-slide the two top cross-slides are located, forming a support for the cutting tool. The lateral and cross-feed motions are derived from the splined feed-shaft. Longitudinal movement of the carriages upon the bed can also be accomplished by means of a rack and pinion. In addition to the taper attachment, the cross slide is fitted with a circular base, 4 feet 4 inches in diameter, graduated in degrees. Each of these carriages weighs 18 tons.

Fig. 30 shows the interior of the sea-coast gun shop of the arsenal, with guns of different caliber under construction. The total length of this shop is 1,000 feet, the south wing is 150 feet wide, and the north wing 130 feet wide by 600 feet long. In the foreground of this illustration a gun is shown being bored and turned in the lathe described.

The steady rests have forged steel jaws, the inner ends, of which are provided with brass concave caps and openings for taking in various sizes, which is accomplished by fitting into the steady rests internal rings containing an extra set of long chuck jaws. The rests consist of

Fig. 30. View of the Interior of the Watervliet Arsenal Gun Shop

a housing in three parts, i.e., base, top, and chuck ring, and are thus arranged to facilitate the removal of the work. They are bolted to T-slots in the bed by large bolts, and are easily moved in a longitudinal direction by hand, by applying a ratchet the upper end of a vertical shaft, which in turn carries a pinion engaging a rack, secured to the front shear, that extends through the entire length of the bed traversed by the rests.

The boring feed, provided with eight different speeds ranging from 0.01 to 0.1 of

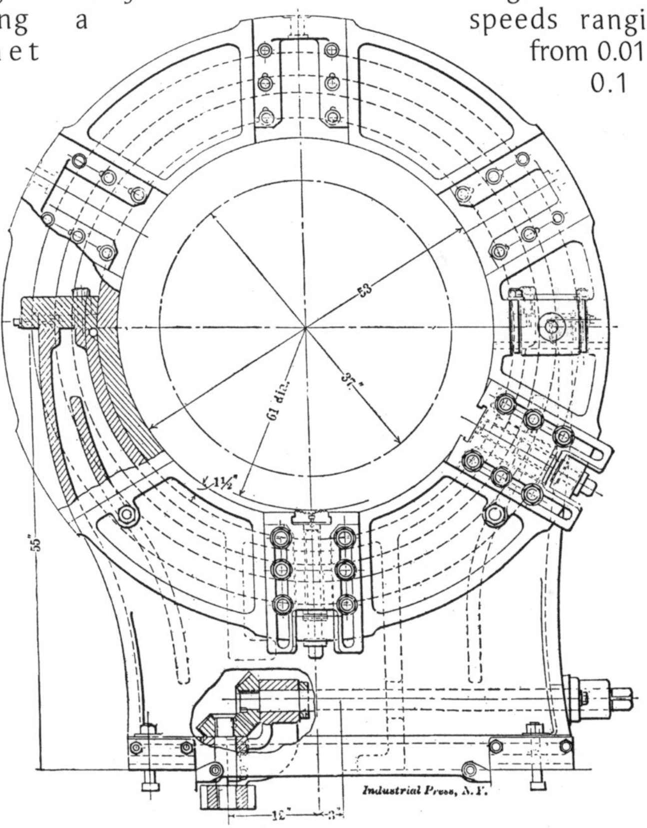

Fig. 31. Partial Section and Front View of Steady Rest for 16-inch Gun Boring Lathe

wrench at the square end of a horizontal transverse shaft (shown in engraving Fig. 31), journaled in the base of the rest. This shaft terminates in a miter gear, engaging a similar gear in an inch per revolution of faceplate, is automatic, positive, and driven by compound gearing from the head-stock through shaft B, Fig. 29. This shaft is 4 1/2 inches in diameter by 137

29

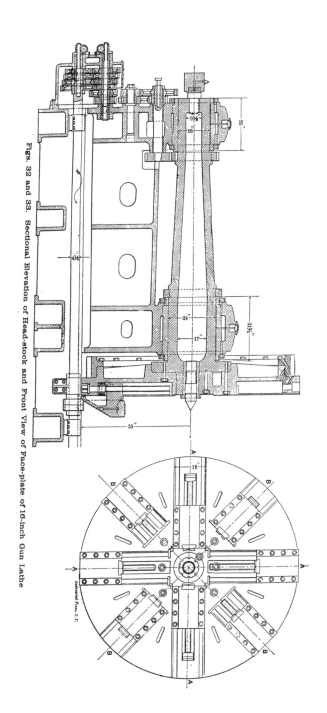

Figs. 32 and 33. Sectional Elevation of Head-stock and Front View of Face-plate of 16-inch Gun Lathe

30

feet long, made in two sections, and engages a worm-wheel and gear on a vertical shaft at the rear of the lathe. The vertical shaft is so arranged as to impart motion to the lead-screw C, Fig. 29, located beneath the boring bar and working in a long bronze nut, clamped to the boring bar carriage. This lead-screw is cut with double lefthand thread, one thread per inch, and is 4 1/2 inches in diameter. For a desired rapid advance or quick return of the boring bar (about 15 feet per minute) when cutting feed is not required, a shaft A., Fig. 29, is operated by means of a hand-wheel at the forward end of the shaft, which is in communication with the friction clutches and pulleys located in the rear of the lathe. The pulleys are driven by a separate line shafting. The boring bar is of forged gun steel, 11 inches in diameter, 61 feet 3 1/2 inches long, with a hole 4 inches diameter throughout the whole length; its weight is equal to 6 tons. The headstock is 23 feet 4 inches long by 9 feet 10 inches wide, and is made in one casting. The cone has five steps for a 10-inch belt and is strongly back-geared, giving a wide range of changes of speed by means of triple gearing to the face-plate.

The main spindle is made of close-grained cast iron, 24 inches diameter at the main journal, and has a bearing in a cast-iron shell 31 3/4 inches long. The rear bearing is similar in construction, but is only 16 inches diameter by 25 1/2 inches in length. The spindle is provided with a flange to which the face-plate is bolted. It is also provided with a thrust bearing of ample surface, with anti-friction washers at the front bearing. The main spindle bearings are made in halves and capped. The face-plate contains slots for clamping the work and has several adjustable steel chuck jaws, shown in Fig. 33, which have V-shaped faces. It also has a cast steel ring gear securely bolted to it. This gear is 10 1/2 inches face, 8 feet 9 1/2 inches outside diameter, by 3.59 inches circular pitch, and serves to drive the face-plate. The face-plate weighs 13 tons.

All boring, reaming, turning and facing operations are performed in the lathe described, the mechanism permitting of boring and turning simultaneously, in order to facilitate rapid progress in construction. The principal remaining operations for the completion of the gun consist mainly in rifling the bore, and threading and slotting the breech. The 16-inch breech-loading rifle boring and turning lathe was designed by the ordnance department and manufactured by the Pond Machine Tool Co., Plainfield, N.J.

Chapter III

Construction Of Deep Hole Drills

It has always been an expensive operation to drill out the interior of a hollow spindle. Indeed, it has not only been an expensive operation, but, on account of the spindle being of high-carbon steel, it has also been a difficult operation. Thus we find on the market hollow-drawn tubing, such as the Shelby tubing, which is intended to be furnished at a less price than one can bore out the interior of a solid bar. Of course, for some purposes this tubing answers very well. But there are many cases, as in certain kinds of spindles, where such tubing cannot be used.

Nearly all lathes nowadays must be built with a hollow spindle. This is also true of spindles of boring machines, drill presses, etc., and thus we have a large variety of work on machine tools which involves deep drilling. The cost of deep drilling has been greatly reduced recently, by several manufacturers, by means of what may be termed a hollow drill. A strong flow of oil is forced through this drill against the cut, and on its return carries the chips with it, thus performing the double function of keeping the drill cool and clearing out the chips.

A perspective view of one of these drills fitted up complete for work, is indicated in Fig. 34. This drill was developed in the shops of the Lodge & Shipley Machine Tool Co., Cincinnati, Ohio, by Mr. N.D. Chard. The body of the drill B is made of machine steel. The point P is made of tool steel, and is held in position by the taper pin ft. A hole H is drilled in the shank, and from this hole the oil is led to slots S, which are milled along the outside. These slots run the full length of the drill, and then shoot down at the ends, as indicated. F is a flat spot for holding the drill.

A longitudinal sectional view of the drill is shown in Fig. 35, from which the construction of the passageway for the oil is better seen. H, again, is the oil inlet hole already referred to. Two small holes J are drilled into it in the manner indicated in this figure. The holes K are then drilled, and a piece of brass tube is bent in the arc of a circle and the ends are entered into the holes J and K. It is then hammered down into place, and the joint is flushed with solder. The slot P is milled out so as to have a semi-circular bottom. Into this slot the cutter or point of the drill is neatly fitted. These points

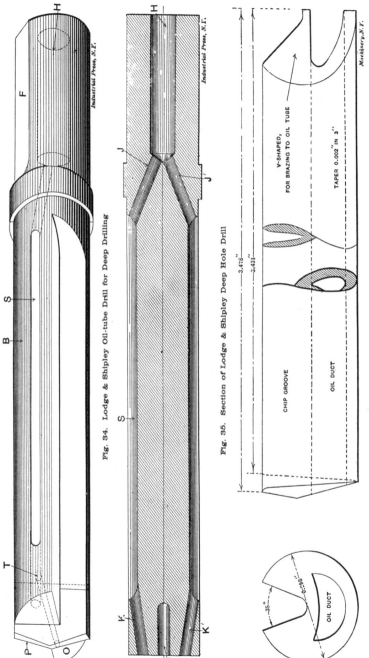

Fig. 34. Lodge & Shipley Oil-tube Drill for Deep Drilling

Industrial Press, N.Y.

Fig. 35. Section of Lodge & Shipley Deep Hole Drill

Industrial Press, N.Y.

Fig. 36. Detail of Deep Hole Drill, 0.303 inch Diameter, Enlarged about Four times Natural Size

Machinery, N.Y.

V-SHAPED, FOR BRAZING TO OIL TUBE

TAPER 0.002″ IN 3″

CHIP GROOVE

OIL DUCT

3.418″

3.431″

OIL DUCT

0.098″

35°

are best made of Novo steel, as they then hold up better under high speed. They are made as screwed onto the end of the spindle, as shown, and a plate *P* holds the spindle up against the

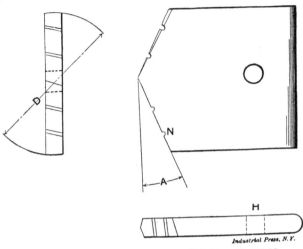

Fig. 37. Detail of Blade Inserted in Drill in Figs. 34 and 35

shown in Fig. 37. The hole *H* in the cutter is reamed through the drill, while the cutter is clamped firmly back against its seat at the end of the slot. The angle *A* is made about 20 degrees. The cutting edge is nicked at several places, as at *N*, in order to break up the chips, this being done on the corner of an emery wheel. After the drill is put into place, it is ground up accurately to the diameter *D*.

The arrangement of a turret machine for boring out lathe spindles with this drill is shown in the illustration in Fig. 38. Instead of the long slide and hexagonal turret, a special slide *A* is provided, which receives the drills. *B* is a steady-rest, and *S* is the spindle. A lathe carrier is center by means of a few bolts. At *C* is shown a Brown & Sharpe No. 2 pump, which is belted up to run 350 revolutions per minute. This gives an ample supply of oil for drilling a three-inch hole. A flexible tube leads from the pump to the fitting *F*, and from thence the oil enters the spindle. The trays *T* catch the oil, and from these trays a pipe leads to the suction side of the pump. The drill is made long enough so as to run a short distance beyond the middle of the spindle to be drilled, the spindle being then turned around and drilled from the other end. With a drill made up in the manner explained, it is possible to drill a 15-16 diameter hole in a 0.40 carbon steel spindle at the rate

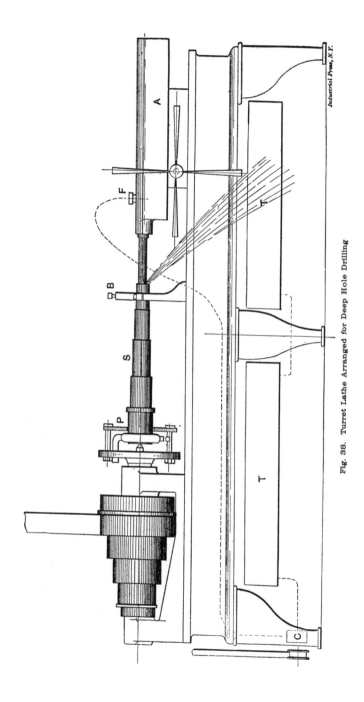

Fig. 38. Turret Lathe Arranged for Deep Hole Drilling

Industrial Press, N.Y.

35

of 1 3/8 inch per minute. The cutting speed would be 60 feet per minute at the largest diameter of the drill.

To Measure the Radii of Deep-hole Drills

Deep-hole drills of the type shown in Fig. 39 should be made so that the cutting edge or lip a of the drill is a radial line,

hole or breaking of the drill. Hence it follows that the location of the center exactly in the cutting edge is very important. A glance at a cross section of the drill, Fig. 39, convinces us that a direct measuring of the drill center cannot be made with ordinary instruments. Hence Ludwig Loewe & Co., of Berlin, Germany, employ for this purpose a special micrometer with

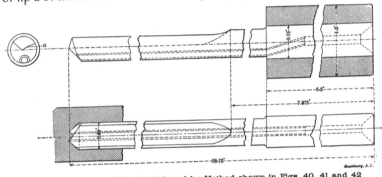

Fig. 39. Type of Deep Hole Drill Gaged by Method shown in Figs. 40, 41 and 42

or in other words, so that it goes exactly through the center of the drill. It is clear that if a drill is made having the cutting edge under the center, a small core of the stock in the center will not be cut off, and will instead tend to remain and form a slender column or thread remaining in the hole. On the other hand, if the cutting edge lies over the center, the center portion cannot be cut out, but will be crushed together, the same as occurs with an ordinary twist drill. In deep hole drilling this is not permissible, as it will very soon cause inaccuracy of the

disks and a V-shaped anvil clock, the principle and use of which is described in the following.

Fig. 40 shows the special micrometer, which measures the radii of deep hole drills up to 60 mm. (2.362 inches). Its construction is the same as that of an ordinary micrometer with a V-point for measuring screw threads, but in addition it has an adjustable V-block which is locked in position by a clamping screw; also, two disks 10 and 30 mm. in diameter are provided. The smaller disk is used for setting the micrometer for drills up to 32 mm., as shown in Fig. 40, and the larger one for drills of 30 to 60 mm. diameter. For measuring drills of small di-

half the diameter of the drill to be measured is multiplied by the constant 1.1045, and the

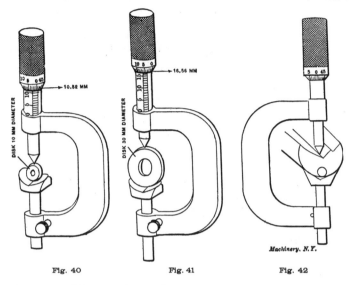

Fig. 40   Fig. 41   Fig. 42

ameter up to 32 mm. the scale of the micrometer is set to 10.52 mm. (5 + 5 X 1.1045), and the disk of 10 mm. diameter is placed in the V-block, after which the block with the disk is pushed against the measuring point and clamped fast in this position, whereupon the preliminary adjustment necessary is completed. For adjusting the micrometer for drills of 30 to 60 mm. diameter, the 30 mm. disk is used in the same manner, but the scale of the micrometer in this case is adjusted to 16.56 mm. (15 X 1.1045). After having found the preliminary adjustment of the V-block for drills up to 32 mm. diameter, as shown in Fig. 40, the radius or

scale of the micrometer adjusted accordingly; or for greater convenience we may use the diagram, Fig. 47, in which we can read off the product of r times 1.1045 without calculation. For example, suppose we wish to measure a drill whose radius is 7.45 mm. We must find the proper reading for the micrometer screw when the drill is laid in the angle block and the point adjusted, as indicated in Fig. 42. Turning to the diagram, Fig. 47, we find in the upper horizontal scale the figure corresponding to 7.45 and trace downward along the vertical line until we reach the diagonal, thence going horizontally from this point toward the right or left, whichever may be convenient, we find in the vertical scale the number 8.2 mm., or the product of 7.45 X 1.1045. Hence, if in measuring the drill of 7.45 mm. radius, we get a micrometer, reading of 8.2 mm., it is known that the apex of the angle of the groove, lies exactly in the center of the drill. To adjust the micrometer for drills from 30 to 60 mm. diameter, the radius of the drill is multiplied by the constant

zontal scale we find the point corresponding to 27.35, and follow the vertical line downward until it intersects the diagonal, thence to the right or left to the vertical where we read 15.2. With this datum, any excess or deficiency of thickness of the drill over the center can be read off directly from the scale. Figs. 43 and 44 are made from photographs showing substantially the same as Figs. 40, 41, and 42.

Figs. 43 and 44. Micrometers for Measuring Radii of Deep Hole Drills

1.1045, and 15 mm. is subtracted from the product, or **r** times 1.1045-15 mm.= micrometer setting. The diagram, Fig. 48, however, saves this calculation and is used in the same manner as Fig. 47. For example, to find the micrometer setting for a drill having a radius of 27.35 mm.: In the upper hori-

Principle of the Gage

The principle of the gage depends upon the proposition that the homologous sides of similar triangles are in direct proportion. Hence in Fig. 45 we have—

$$\frac{r}{l} = \frac{r_1}{l_1} = \frac{r_2}{l_2}, \text{ etc.}$$

Therefore the values of l_1 and l_2 are easy to determine, since

$$l = \frac{r}{\sin a}$$

in which r corresponds to the sin

16.56 mm., instead of 31.56 mm., in order to make the scope of the micrometer include the larger drills without the need of making a larger frame. The prin-

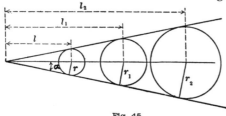

Fig. 45

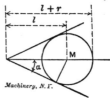

Machinery, N. Y.

Fig. 46

a radius of the drill, and a = 1/2 the constant angle of the V-block of the micrometer,- whence we derive the constant 1.1045.

It will be observed that the product of the radius by the constant is used directly when setting for drills 32 mm. or less diameter, but that when measuring drills of 30 to 60 mm. diameter the product is diminished by 15 mm. This is because in setting to the 30 mm. disk, the micrometer screw is adjusted to

ciple is illustrated in Fig. 46. For the disk M we reckon

$$l + r = \frac{r}{\sin a} + r$$

Hence if one sets the screw of the micrometer to this measure, and pushes the V-block with the disk M resting in it, until the disk is found to be in perceptible contact with the measuring point of the screw and there clamps it fast, the gage is adjusted. The proof of the correctness of the setting is that if we

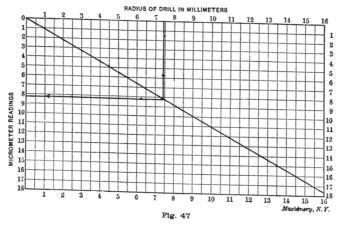

Fig. 47

put back the micrometer screw equal to l + r then will the point of the screw lie in the vertex of the angle a. In other words, the lengths l, l_1, and l_2 will be exactly indicated without calculation.

The method of measuring the deep hole drills above described may be of suggestive value not only when measuring deep hole drills, but for many other occasions where it is not spindle being pointed a little less than the included angle of groove in drill, which is about 38 degrees, as shown in Fig. 36.

In making these drills, half-inch Novo stock is cut into lengths of, about 4 inches, Fig. 49; then a hole is drilled through the center; next the piece is heated and struck up in dies S S_1, which operation forms a groove and forces the center

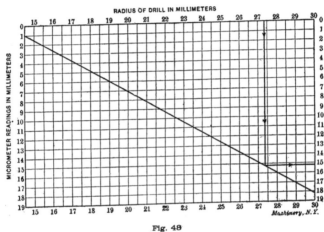

Fig. 48

possible to take direct measurements with ordinary micrometers.

Another Type of Deep Hole Drill

The type of drill shown and described in the following differs in some essentials from the types already described. In the factory where it is used, a plain, everyday micrometer is used for gaging it, the end of the measuring point on the micrometer hole below the center into a crescent shape, as shown. It is then "pack annealed"; then both ends are pointed to 60 degrees, and turned in a lathe on female centers to within 0.010 inch of finished size, this being allowed for grinding. After being pointed, the work is held in a milling machine vise and the groove is finished with the cutter shown in the upper right-hand corner in Fig. 49. The groove is milled to a depth equal to one-half the finished diam-

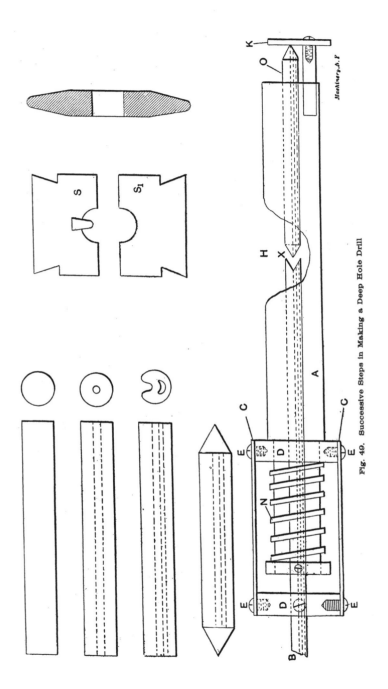

Fig. 49. Successive Steps in Making a Deep Hole Drill

Machinery, N. Y.

41

eter, plus 0.005 inch, minus the amount to be ground out of the groove, which varies according to the size of the drill and the grade of steel used. In short, the bottom of the groove must be exactly central when the drill is finished.

The drill is hardened two-thirds of its length, and the outside and groove are ground. It is now placed in a brazing fixture, as shown in the bottom view in Fig. 49. A is a body of suitable length with a hole drilled through it to accommodate all sizes of drills under 1/2 inch. B is a steel tube a little under the size of the drill; a groove is rolled the whole length of B to conform with the shape of the groove in the drill.

brought together at the opening H, which is milled out to allow point X to come in contact with the flame. A small wooden plug is fitted into O and B to prevent the brazing stopping up the oil-hole. A small piece of silver solder is placed between the two ends; then the swinging stop K is moved into place against the end of drill O. Collars DD are held together by strips C and screws E. Now B and O are brought together at X and are held firmly in place by the stop K and tension of spring N, B being held by D with the set-screw shown. With this rig, the brazing of the tube and drill is satisfactorily accomplished, the device insuring correct alignment.

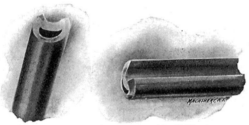

Fig. 50. Two Views of the Drill

A V-groove is milled in the end of the tube to fit the back end of the drill. Collars DD are bored out, one a loose fit on A, the other on B.

The drill O is placed in the end of A, then B is inserted into the other end of A. The two are

This type of deep hole drill is far superior to the old drill with round oil hole, it being cheaper to make, at the same time as the crescent-shaped hole allows a greater flow of oil at the cutting edge.

Deep-hole Drilling

Machinery Magazine – August 5, 1926 by F.W.B

Some interesting results are often obtained in drilling deep holes in the barrels of shotguns and rifles. For example, cores such as shown at A and B in the accompanying illustration are sometimes obtained in drilling shotgun barrels. These cores, or "wires" were produced in drilling two shotgun barrels, each 30 inches long. The core shown at A, obtained from one barrel, was 30 inches long and 1/8-inch in diameter. The cross shade marks at irregular intervals indicate the points at which the drill was removed for sharpening. This frequent sharpening was necessary, as the drill did not have a sufficient amount of clearance at the centre, and this fault could not be remedied until the hole already started was finished. After the drill had been sharpened it would cut freely for a depth of about 1/2-inch, and the cutting edge would then become dull, so the sleeve which rotated the gun barrel was stopped. The diameter of the hole drilled in this case was 0.685-inch.

The making of the core A was the result of grinding the drill groove, by mistake, 1/16-inch below centre, for the whole length of the drill, as indicated in the diagram at C. This caused the drill to have the same action as a hollow mill, the tooth or point leaving the core N. The greater the depth of the groove below centre, the larger will be the diameter of the core. The radius of the groove should always be equal to or greater than the distance the groove is cut below the centre, in order for the drill to cut freely and not ring the walls of the hole.

Referring to view D, which shows a side elevation of the drill point and a cross section of the work being drilled, it will be noted that the high point P of the drill is located at a distance Q from the centre about which the work revolves. This explains the formation of the rivet-shaped head on the end of the core A.

At F is shown diagrammatically the point of the drill as it appears when ground to cut freely. The letters N, P, and Q indicate, respectively, the core, the high point of the drill, and

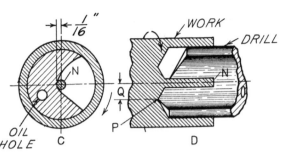

the distance of the point P from the centre about which the work revolves. These references are the same as in view D except that Q, in view D, is indicated on the work and not in its true position on the drill. At E is shown the end view of a drill, the groove of which was not ground out to a radius equal to the radius of the core, as is necessary to provide free cutting.

At B is shown a core several inches longer than the work from which it was removed. It shows a spiral effect for more than one-half its length, and a division of the core with a fine end R branching off from the

splitting of the core was caused by the groove in the drill being too deep and the oil-hole drilled too near the centre, which left a very thin web between the oil-hole and the groove. The pressure of the work caused this web to crack, and eventually it broke out and sheared the stock until the rotating work stopped. The drill was then removed and resharpened, after which it cut the smooth portion of the core shown at the left-hand end.

At H is shown a shotgun barrel which is only partly drilled and has a core projecting several inches from the end. In one case, a core 30 inches long and

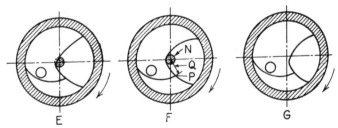

main part. The spiral groove is also shown on the main part where the fine end was forced out. The spiral effect and the

1/32-inch in diameter was obtained from a 30-inch shotgun barrel when it had been drilled only half way through. When

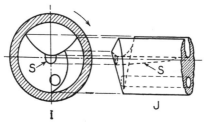

the drill was resharpened and the drilling of the hole completed, another core of the same length as the first one was produced. The second core had a head at the end where the point of the drill broke through the work. With the same drill, cores 60 inches long and 1/32-inch in diameter were obtained in drilling 30-inch shotgun barrels. The writer kept two of the 60-inch cores and two of the 30-inch cores for some time. These cores were often examined with considerable interest by visitors.

On conducting an investigation to determine the conditions resulting in producing cores that were longer than the work drilled, the writer found that the groove as shown at G was not milled to the centre of the drill. In order to make the drill cut, it had been ground out at the point, as indicated in the views I and J. The groove S was ground deeper than necessary, however, being 1/64-inch below the centre at the point of the

drill and tapering back to the milled-surface. As the depth of the hole increased and the core became longer, the tapered groove caused the core to be bent to and fro with a twisting motion at every revolution of the work. This motion is indicated by the dotted lines in view M, and was the action which caused the cores to be stretched or drawn out. The speed of the work when the 60-inch cores were produced was approximately 900 revolutions per minute.

Some workmen eliminate the necessity of having the drill groove ground to the centre by cutting away the drill point, as indicated in views K and L. The clearance part of the end of the drill is ground away to a depth of 1/4-inch below the cutting or lid part of the drill. The straight side of the ground away portion passes through the centre of the drill. This produces a cutting lip of somewhat differ-

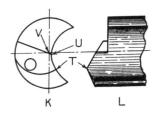

K   L

0.002-to 0.003-inch below the centre. This would result in the production of a core 0.004- to 0.006-inch in diameter, which would be kept broken up by the

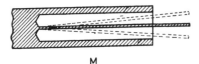

M

ent shape, which extends from the outer point *T* to the point *U*, and from there to the point *V*, as illustrated. In order to obtain the best results, the groove in a deep-hole drill should be about chips and would not, therefore, clog up the chip passage, as would a core of larger diameter.

Deep-Hole Drill

MACHINERY MAGAZINE – MARCH 10, 1927 BY F.C.M

While there is nothing new in the general principle involved in deep-hole drilling, the equipment employed has been greatly improved within the last few years. The drill made up from the parts shown in the accompanying illustration is an example of an improved type of deep-hole drill in which interesting constructional features are incorporated. This drill is designed for use in drilling holes 9/32-inch in diameter by 15 1/2 inches deep. The straightness of the drilled holes must not vary more than 1/32-inch in the total length of 15-1/2 inches. The drills are used in a standard upright small-bore rifle-barrel drilling machine.

The drilling machine rotates the work, and the drill remains stationary. In order to operate satisfactorily, a machine of this kind must be designed to maintain accurate alignment of the drill. The machine must have provision for supplying an ample quantity of oil at a pressure of from 1,200 to 1,500 lb. per square inch. This high oil pressure is required in order to prevent the chips from clogging and to carry them out through the chip groove. Even when every precaution has been taken, a drill will occasionally become clogged, and in order to prevent breakage in such instances, an automatic kick-out should be provided which is designed to stop the motor and thereby prevent the drill from being twisted off. Breakage, however, cannot be entirely eliminated by any safety device.

Drills of the design shown

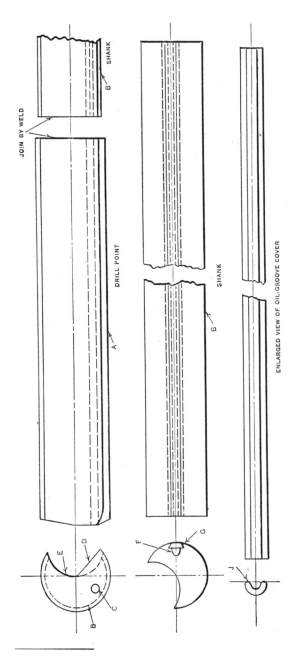

Parts of Deep-hole Drill

in the illustration run at a speed of 1,200 revolutions per minute, with a feed of 0.001-inch per revolution, which makes it possible to drill at the rate of 1.2 inches per minute. The drill point shown at A is made of high-speed steel. The oil passage C is drilled through the point.

The chip groove is shown at E, and the cutting lip at D. The shank B of the drill is made of 1/4-inch drill rod, having a dovetail slot G milled along its length above the oil-groove F, which connects with the oil-hole C in point A. The oil-groove is covered by a strip of copper J, which is riveted or swaged into the dovetail slot.

The strip J, which is shown to an enlarged scale, is made from round copper wire by rolling a groove in one side, thus producing a strip having a cres-cent shape cross-section. The high-speed steel point A is welded to the drill rod shank B without closing the drilled oil passage C in the high-speed steel point. The welding is done by means of an oxy-acetylene torch after the point is hardened. The copper strip is swaged into place in the dovetail slot after the welding operation by means of a small high. speed riveting machine. No difficulty has ever been experienced from breakage at the weld or from the blowing out of the copper strip, even though pressures up to 1,500 lb. are constantly maintained. The final operation in making the deep-hole drill is that of straightening and grinding to size. It may be of interest to note that the cost of this drill was considerably less than the regular commercial type, which is more usually employed.